Clarinet part

the best of grade

Clarinet

A compilation of the best Grade 1 clarinet pieces ever selected by the major examination boards

Selected and edited by Paul Harris

 FABER ***ff*** MUSIC

© 2010 by Faber Music Ltd
This edition first published in 2010
Bloomsbury House 74–77 Great Russell Street London WC1B 3DA
Music processed by Jackie Leigh
Design by Økvik Design
Printed in England by Caligraving Ltd

ISBN10: 0-571-53421-X
EAN13: 978-0-571-53421-0

To buy Faber Music publications or to find out about the full range of titles available
please contact your local music retailer or Faber Music sales enquiries:

Faber Music Limited, Burnt Mill, Elizabeth Way, Harlow CM20 2HX
Tel: +44 (0)1279 82 89 82   Fax: +44 (0)1279 82 89 83
sales@fabermusic.com   fabermusic.com

The text paper used in this publication is a virgin fibre product that is manufactured in the UK
to ISO 14001 standards. The wood fibre used is only sourced from managed forests using
sustainable forestry principles. This paper is 100% recyclable.

All audio tracks recorded in London, February 2010
Performed by Paul Harris (Clarinet) and Robin Bigwood (Piano)

Engineered by Robin Bigwood; Produced by Fiona Bolton
℗ 2010 Faber Music Ltd © 2010 Faber Music Ltd

Contents

The performers

Paul Harris studied with John Davies at the Royal Academy of Music, and has gone on to establish an international reputation as teacher, composer and writer. His publications include the best-selling *Clarinet Basics* and highly acclaimed *Improve your sight-reading!* series.

Robin Bigwood is a freelance pianist and harpsichordist, performing with Passacaglia, Feinstein Ensemble, Britten Sinfonia and as a soloist. He also works as a sound engineer and producer.

Track 1: Tuning note B (Concert A)

Song of the Volga Boatmen
from 'First Book of Clarinet Solos'

PERFORMANCE [2]
ACCOMPANIMENT [3]

There are lots of opportunities to create contrast in the dynamic colour within this piece.
Play with a rich and warm tone, and make sure you sustain the sound through every note.

Traditional
arr. Paul Reade

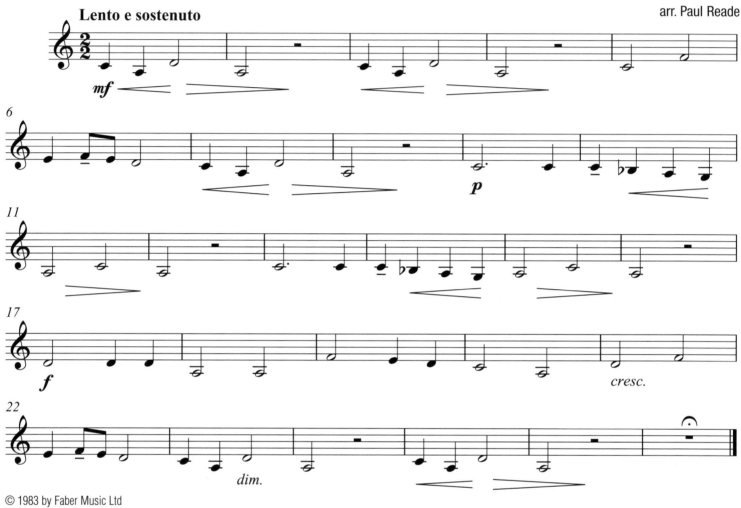

Daisy, Daisy
from 'Clarinet Basics'

PERFORMANCE [4]
ACCOMPANIMENT [5]

Music-hall songs used to be sung with tremendous energy and enthusiasm—can you
convey this as you play this piece? Think in four-bar phrases and sustain the tone
throughout the long notes.

Traditional
arr. Paul Harris

LIST A (ABRSM 2007 and Trinity Guildhall 2007–11)

Riding on a Donkey

from 'First Book of Clarinet Solos'

PERFORMANCE 6
ACCOMPANIMENT 7

This piece was originally a 'work song', sung to help pass the time during hard physical labour. The first beat of each phrase should be played firmly and the f passages should convey a strong and robust feel.

Traditional
arr. Paul Reade

Lullaby
from 'The Really Easy Clarinet Book'

PERFORMANCE [8]
ACCOMPANIMENT [9]

Aim to create a gentle, flowing sound to bring this lullaby to life. Allow the tempo to broaden a
little around bars 11 and 12 and sleep to befall at the end.

Carl Maria von Weber (1786–1826)
arr. Paul Harris

Andante con moto

LIST A (ABRSM 2008–13)

Minuet
from 'Easy Pieces for Clarinet and Piano'

PERFORMANCE [10]
ACCOMPANIMENT [11]

Placing a slight emphasis on the first beat of each bar will give the Minuet spirit and character.
Switch to a more sustained and richly *legato* playing style for the middle section.

Ludwig van Beethoven (1770–1827)
arr. Robin de Smet

Allegretto

FINE

D.C. al Fine

Time to Go

from 'Clarinet All Sorts'

An expressive and flowing sound is required, so tongue the first note of each slur very gently.
Give the quavers space and support the tone through the longer notes.

James Rae

The Drunken Sailor

from 'The Really Easy Clarinet Book'

PERFORMANCE 14
ACCOMPANIMENT 15

A lively sea shanty, play this piece with lots of energy. Employ a light, crisp tongue action and explore dynamic contrast by following the instruction to repeat.

Traditional
arr. Paul Harris

To be played with repeat

Pierrot

from 'First Book of Clarinet Solos'

PERFORMANCE 16
ACCOMPANIMENT 17

Pierrot is a clown so play this piece with a sense of fun and high spirits. Feel the notes bounce along and create a distinct contrast at the *mp* marking to give the piece extra musical colour.

Traditional
arr. Paul Reade

To be played with repeat

*This piece appears on List A of the Trinity Guildhall 2007–2011 syllabus

Cowkeeper's Tune

from 'The Really Easy Clarinet Book'

PERFORMANCE 18
ACCOMPANIMENT 19

Be careful where you breathe so you don't spoil the musical phrases of this flowing and expressive piece. For example, take your first breath between the notes in bar 8.

Traditional
arr. Paul Harris

Moderato

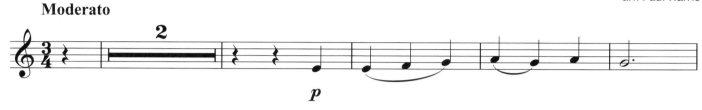

Promenade

from 'Summer Sketches'

PERFORMANCE ⟨20⟩
ACCOMPANIMENT ⟨21⟩

A good-humoured, care-free and engaging tune, allow this to move fluently forward with a one-in-a-bar feel. The *f* needn't be too loud but should create a marked contrast to the lyrical *p* of the middle section.

Paul Harris

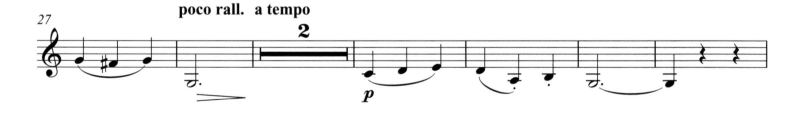

Piano accompaniment

the best of grade 1
Clarinet

Selected and edited by Paul Harris

FABER *ff* MUSIC

Contents

© 2010 by Faber Music Ltd
This edition first published in 2010
Bloomsbury House 74–77 Great Russell Street London WC1B 3DA
Music processed by Jackie Leigh
Design by Økvik Design
Printed in England by Caligraving Ltd
All rights reserved

ISBN10: 0-571-53421-X
EAN13: 978-0-571-53421-0

Song of the Volga Boatmen

from 'First Book of Clarinet Solos'

Traditional
arr. Paul Reade

Daisy, Daisy

from 'Clarinet Basics'

Traditional
arr. Paul Harris

Riding on a Donkey

from 'First Book of Clarinet Solos'

Traditional
arr. Paul Reade

Lullaby

from 'The Really Easy Clarinet Book'

Carl Maria von Weber (1786–1826)
arr. Paul Harris

Minuet

from 'Easy Pieces for Clarinet and Piano'

PERFORMANCE 10
ACCOMPANIMENT 11

Ludwig van Beethoven (1770–1827)
arr. Robin de Smet

Time to Go

from 'Clarinet All Sorts'

PERFORMANCE ⑫
ACCOMPANIMENT ⑬

James Rae

Moderato

The Drunken Sailor

from 'The Really Easy Clarinet Book'

Traditional
arr. Paul Harris

To be played with repeat

Pierrot
from 'First Book of Clarinet Solos'

Traditional
arr. Paul Reade

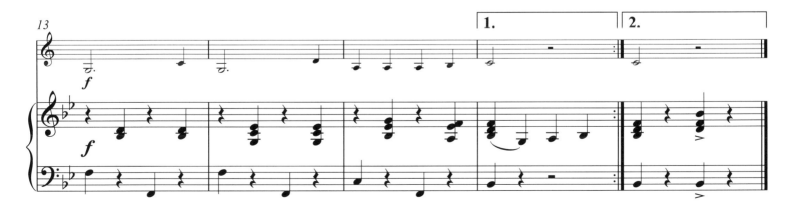

To be played with repeat

*This piece appears on List A of the Trinity Guildhall 2007–2011 syllabus

Cowkeeper's Tune

from 'The Really Easy Clarinet Book'

Traditional
arr. Paul Harris

Promenade

from 'Summer Sketches'

Paul Harris

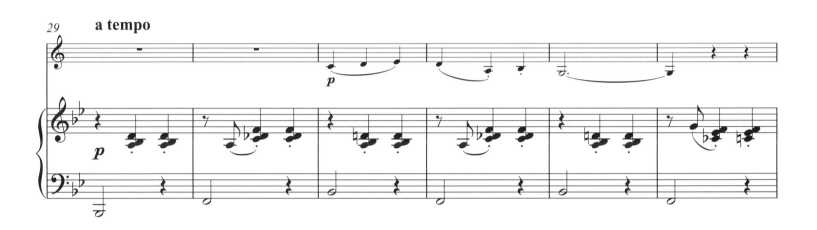

Welcome to …

Paul Harris's
Clarinet Basics

Clarinet Basics is a landmark method by one of the leading figures in clarinet education. It starts at absolute beginner level and progresses to about Grade 2 level. The method is set out in 22 stages, each of which includes:

- a wonderful variety of concert pieces from the great composers

- traditional tunes and fun, original exercises

- 'finger gyms' and 'warm ups' to help establish a sound technique

- invaluable 'fact files' and 'quizzes' to teach notation and general musicianship

- helpful, clear 'fingering charts' and 'rhythm boxes'

- great illustrations!

The separate teacher's book contains clarinet and piano accompaniments, suggestions for group work and teaching tips.

Clarinet Basics (pupil's book) ISBN 0-571-51814-1
Clarinet Basics (pupil's book with CD) ISBN 0-571-52282-3
Clarinet Basics (teacher's book) ISBN 0-571-51815-X
Clarinet Basics (accompaniment CD) ISBN 0-571-52167-3
Clarinet Basics Repertoire ISBN 0-571-52254-8

To buy Faber Music publications or to find out about the full range of titles available
please contact your local music retailer or Faber Music sales enquiries:

Faber Music Ltd, Burnt Mill, Elizabeth Way, Harlow CM20 2HX
Tel: +44 (0) 1279 82 89 82   Fax: +44 (0) 1279 82 89 83
sales@fabermusic.com   fabermusic.com   expressprintmusic.com

Study No.5

PERFORMANCE 22

from '80 Graded Studies for Clarinet Book One'

Give this gentle study a waltz-like character. Add your own dynamic levels to shape the phrases
(e.g. *f* in bars 9–10 and *p* in bars 11–12); a *rit.* in bars 23–24 would complete the piece musically.

Friedrich Demnitz (1845–1890)

Hornpipe Study

PERFORMANCE 23

from 'Clarinet Basics'

A hornpipe is a vigorous sailor's dance, so lots of energy is needed here. Play the accented
notes with real enthusiasm. Consider adddding a slight *rit.* in bar 12 then picking up the tempo
again for the final section.

Paul Harris

Study No.30

PERFORMANCE 24

from 'Jazz Clarinet Studies'

There are lots of ingredients to enjoy here. Think about how you're going to bring the different markings to life.

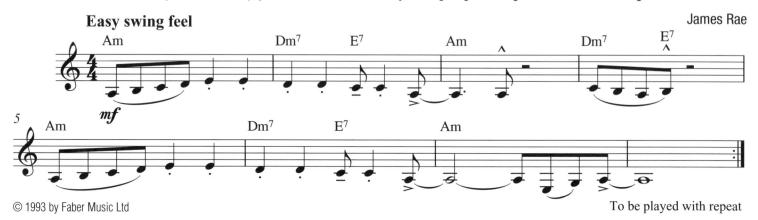

Easy swing feel

James Rae

To be played with repeat

Study No.31

PERFORMANCE 25

from 'Jazz Clarinet Studies'

There's only one dynamic marking in this piece so add some more of your own. Be it a haunted house or a cat creeping along an alley, have your own picture in mind when playing this study.

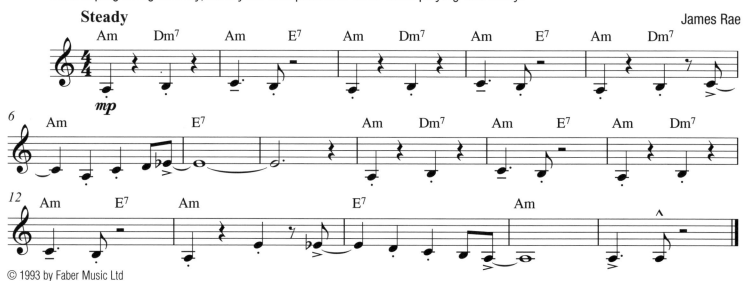

Steady

James Rae

Study No.32

PERFORMANCE 26

from 'Jazz Clarinet Studies'

There's only a small difference between these two lines—be sure to make it clear in your performance.

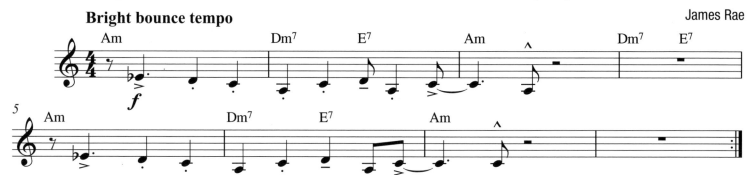

Bright bounce tempo

James Rae

To be played with repeat